W0009050

1906248508
ISBN

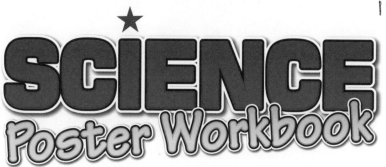

THE SAME POSTERS USED IN
35,000 SCHOOLS WORLDWIDE!

Dear Teacher,

Daydream Education's Science Poster Workbooks are an ideal starter or summary activity. This simple and effective reference book will also help with revision and homework assignments.

The colourful and engaging book contains 30 of Daydream Education's Award-Winning wall charts. Accompanied by 300 quiz questions, the Poster Workbook will test knowledge and understanding of key curriculum topics at Key Stage 2.

IDEAL STARTER OR SUMMARY ACTIVITY

Quantity	10+	25+	50+
Price (per book)	£2.95	£2.50	£1.95

Why not take advantage of our fantastic discounts and purchase Poster Workbooks for your class? You could even sell them onto your pupils as a visual learning guide that can be used at home, as well as in the classroom.

To order your Science Poster Workbooks, simply photocopy and complete the order form in the enclosed book. The book is a gift and you are under no obligation to purchase the product.

We look forward to hearing from you.

Craig Moss
Customer Relations Manager

Quiz

Circle the correct answers.

1 What does the heart do to blood?

a) Makes   b) Changes   c) Pumps

2 What do veins carry back to the heart?

a) Water   b) Blood   c) Air

3 The heart is an organ and is also a…?

a) bone   b) muscle   c) limb

4 Which parts of the heart open and close?

a) Valves   b) Chambers   c) Arteries

5 What does 'oxygenated' mean?

a) Contains Oxygen   b) Lacks Oxygen   c) Needs Oxygen

6 Oxygenated blood comes from the…?

a) veins   b) valves   c) lungs

7 How many valves are there in the heart?

a) 3   b) 4   c) 7

8 What does 'deoxygenated' mean?

a) Contains Oxygen   b) Lacks Oxygen   c) Needs Oxygen

9 To where do veins carry blood?

a) The Body   b) The Heart   c) The Lungs

10 Deoxygenated blood comes from the…?

a) body   b) arteries   c) veins

How many have you answered correctly? /10

TEETH

We use our teeth to cut, crush and tear food.

INCISORS
These are used to bite and cut food.

CANINES
These are used to tear food.

PREMOLARS
These are used to crush and grind soft food.

MOLARS
These are used to crush and grind hard food.

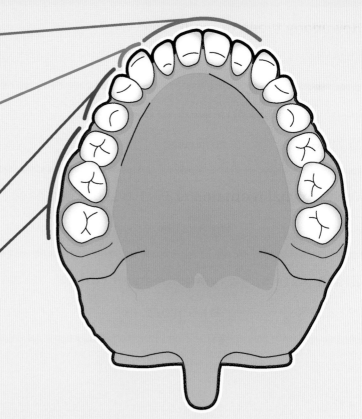

We have two sets of teeth in our lifetime. When we are very young we have milk teeth which fall out and are then replaced by permanent teeth.

REMEMBER

Visit your dentist at least every 6 months.

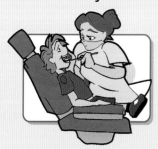

Eat less sugary food.

Brush your teeth morning and night to remove plaque and to protect your gums.

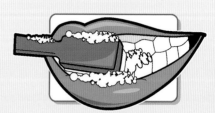

Sugar and other foods are eaten by bacteria which produce plaque. Plaque damages the enamel outer layer of our teeth and attacks our gums. This can be very painful!

Quiz

Circle the correct answers.

1 How many types of teeth are there?

   a) 2   b) 4   c) 6

2 We have two sets of natural teeth in our lifetime.

   a) True   b) False

3 What special teeth do very young children have?

   a) Baby Teeth   b) False Teeth   c) Milk Teeth

4 Brushing teeth regularly removes . . . ?

   a) plaque   b) shellac   c) enamel

5 Which part of a tooth does plaque damage?

   a) Dentine   b) Root   c) Enamel

6 How many teeth does a person usually have?

   a) 16   b) 28   c) 32

7 What attacks gums?

   a) Saliva   b) Milk   c) Plaque

8 What part of a tooth is fixed in the jawbone?

   a) Root   b) Dentine   c) Enamel

9 How many times each year should you visit your dentist?

   a) One   b) Two   c) Ten

10 What forms the main part of the tooth?

   a) Enamel   b) Dentine   c) Filling

How many have you answered correctly?

/10

THE FOOD PYRAMID

The food pyramid below shows the foods that we can eat more of in the green section and the foods that we should eat less of in the red section.

FATS, OILS & SWEETS

EAT SPARINGLY

MEAT, POULTRY, FISH, EGGS, DRY BEANS & NUT GROUPS

2-3 SERVINGS

FRUIT GROUP

2-4 SERVINGS

BREAD, CEREAL, RICE & PASTA GROUPS

6-11 SERVINGS

MILK, YOGURT & CHEESE GROUPS

2-3 SERVINGS

VEGETABLE GROUP

2-4 SERVINGS

COLA

CHOCOLATE

YOGURT

MILK

CORN FLAKES

EAT LESS OF

EAT MORE OF

Remember: All food should be eaten in moderation.

Quiz

THE FOOD PYRAMID

Circle the correct answers.

1 Of which of these foods should you consume less?

a) Cereals   b) Sweets   c) Vegetables

2 Of which of these foods should you consume more?

a) Apples   b) Tea/Coffee   c) Fries

3 Of which of these foods should you consume less?

a) Carrots   b) Eggs   c) Cakes

4 What does 'moderation' mean?

a) More   b) Less   c) Reasonable Amount

5 Most healthy foods are natural.

a) True   b) False

6 Which of these is in apples?

a) Fat   b) Sugar   c) Protein

7 Which of these keeps you healthy?

a) Vitriol   b) Vitamins   c) Viruses

8 Sugar gives you energy and is found in . . . ?

a) butter   b) milk   c) fruit

9 A pint of milk every day gives you nearly all the calcium you need.

a) True   b) False

10 How many food types make up a balanced diet?

a) 4   b) 6   c) 8

How many have you answered correctly?

/10

11

HEALTH RISKS

There are many substances available that can cause us harm. Some change our personality or behaviour, while others can make us dependent and even cause ill health or death.

Alcohol

Although legal, drinking large amounts of alcohol damages the heart, liver, stomach, brain and other organs.

Solvents

Solvents such as glue and correction fluid can be addictive, may cause brain damage and can kill.

Drugs

Sometimes drugs are needed in order to cure an illness. Others are illegal but misuse of both can be dangerous.

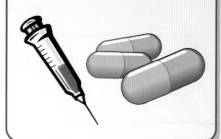

Smoking

Smoking tobacco is legal but is also addictive; it can cause cancer, heart attacks and breathing problems.

Diet

All foods need to be eaten in moderation. Eating lots of fatty or sugary foods can cause strokes, heart disease and obesity.

Fitness

Keeping fit is important because a lack of exercise can weaken muscles such as the heart and lungs. Exercise is also a good way to reduce body fat.

Quiz

HEALTH RISKS

Circle the correct answers.

1. Which of the following damages your health?

   a) Exercise   b) Reading   c) Smoking

2. Smoking tobacco can help cure breathing problems.

   a) True   b) False

3. Which of the following activities will help reduce body fat?

   a) Drinking alcohol   b) Swimming   c) Eating sugary foods

4. Lack of exercise will . . . ?

   a) strengthen muscles   b) weaken muscles   c) improve your health

5. Which of the following can cause heart disease?

   a) Eating lots of fatty foods   b) Playing computer games   c) Sun bathing

6. Alcohol is good for your liver.

   a) True   b) False

7. Drinking large amounts of alcohol will. . . ?

   a) damage your body's organs   b) make you stronger   c) help your digestive system

8. Brain damage can be caused by . . . ?

   a) sniffing glue   b) shopping   c) eating vegetables

9. What can be used to cure illnesses?

   a) Solvents   b) Chocolate   c) Prescribed Drugs

10. Are all drugs good for you?

    a) Yes   b) No

How many have you answered correctly? /10

WHY EXERCISE?

Regular physical activity is very important for all people who want to lead a healthy and fulfilling life. Here are some of the reasons why.

Exercise increases your energy.

Exercise increases your strength and muscle tone.

Exercise helps you sleep more restfully.

Exercise burns off unwanted calories.

Exercise improves your circulation.
This enables all the organs and muscles in your body to work efficiently.

Exercise helps your joints stay loose and supple.

Exercise improves endurance.
The more you do, the more you will be able to do.

Exercise helps relieve stress.
It also enables you to cope with high-pressure situations.

Exercise helps provide you with a good posture.

Exercise increases your ability to concentrate and learn.

Exercise makes you happy.
It improves your state of mind as well as your self-confidence.

Quiz

WHY EXERCISE?

Circle the correct answers.

1. Regular physical activity is . . . . ?

   a) boring   b) unhealthy   c) important for a healthy life

2. What effect does exercise have on muscle tone?

   a) Increases it   b) Decreases it   c) Has no effect

3. Which of the following will help improve circulation?

   a) Eating   b) Reading   c) Running

4. Exercise helps you sleep?

   a) True   b) False

5. Which of the following activities will help improve physical endurance?

   a) Smoking   b) Arguing   c) Swimming

6. When you exercise, your body . . . . ?

   a) creates calories   b) burns calories   c) gains calories

7. Regular exercise will make you . . . . ?

   a) stronger   b) weaker

8. Which of the following activities will help your joints stay loose and supple?

   a) Cycling   b) Watching TV   c) Eating

9. Exercise is a good way to help relieve stress?

   a) True   b) False

10. Regular exercise will . . . . ?

    a) stop you learning   b) help you concentrate   c) cause acne

How many have you answered correctly?

/10

PARTS OF A PLANT

FLOWER / PETALS

The reproductive organs of a plant are in the flower.
Flowers are usually colourful and sometimes smell to help attract insects.

BUD

In the bud, small leaves or flowers start to grow.
The bud protects them.

LEAF

The green chlorophyll in the leaves helps to make food by absorbing sunlight. The energy of the sunlight converts carbon dioxide from the air, and water from the roots, into food for the plant. (photosynthesis)

STEM

The stem's function is to hold the plant upright. It also carries water, minerals and food between the roots and the leaves and flowers.

ROOT

The root anchors the plant in the ground, so that it does not blow away.

ROOT HAIRS

The root hairs help the root to absorb water and minerals from the soil. Water is essential for photosynthesis in the leaves.

Quiz

PARTS OF A PLANT

Circle the correct answers.

1. What anchors a plant into the ground?

   a) Root   b) Stem   c) Bud

2. What are the colourful parts of flowers called?

   a) Grass   b) Stems   c) Petals

3. Green plants make food in a process called . . . ?

   a) respiration   b) meiosis   c) photosynthesis

4. Which part of a plant absorbs water from the ground?

   a) Stem   b) Root Hairs   c) Leaves

5. What chemical makes plants green?

   a) Chlorophyll   b) Chloroform   c) Chlorine

6. Where does photosynthesis occur?

   a) Roots   b) Stems   c) Leaves

7. Which gas is used in photosynthesis?

   a) Carbon Dioxide   b) Hydrogen   c) Oxygen

8. What provides protection for new growth?

   a) Insects   b) A Bud   c) A Flower

9. What carries water, minerals and food between roots and leaves?

   a) Insects   b) Stem   c) Soil

10. Which of these does a plant need to grow well?

    a) Light   b) Cold   c) Dark

How many have you answered correctly?

/10

17

LIFE CYCLE OF A PLANT

Reproduction is the process by which a plant produces seeds to make a new plant. This life cycle shows the different stages in plant reproduction.

FLOWER
The plant grows and develops a flower.

POLLINATION
Pollen is carried from the anther to the stigma.

GERMINATION
The seeds start to grow when they reach a suitable place.

The life cycle of a plant

SEED DISPERSAL
Seeds need to spread out so that they can grow with less competition from each other.

FERTILISATION
Seeds develop when the male sex cells (pollen) fuse with the female sex cells.

Quiz

Circle the correct answers.

1. Which of these carries pollen?

   a) Worm   b) Bee   c) Dog

2. In pollination, the pollen is carried from the anther to the . . . ?

   a) stamen   b) stigma   c) petal

3. How many stages are involved in plant reproduction?

   a) 4   b) 5   c) 6

4. What does 'dispersal' mean?

   a) Spreading Out   b) Throwing   c) Dropping

5. Another name for the male sex cells of a plant is . . . ?

   a) sperm   b) eggs   c) pollen

6. By which process does a plant produce seeds to make a new plant?

   a) Photosynthesis   b) Fertilisation   c) Reproduction

7. When pollen is carried from the anther to the stigma, it is known as . . . ?

   a) pollination   b) fertilisation   c) germination

8. The joining together of a male and female sex cell is called . . . ?

   a) pollination   b) fertilisation   c) germination

9. In germination, what do seeds do?

   a) Join Together   b) Nothing   c) Start to Grow

10. With what sort of cells does pollen fuse?

    a) Male sex cells   b) Female sex cells

How many have you answered correctly? /10

PARTS OF A FLOWER

Flowers may look different but they have similar parts.
Each part has a very important job to do
in the life cycle of a flower.

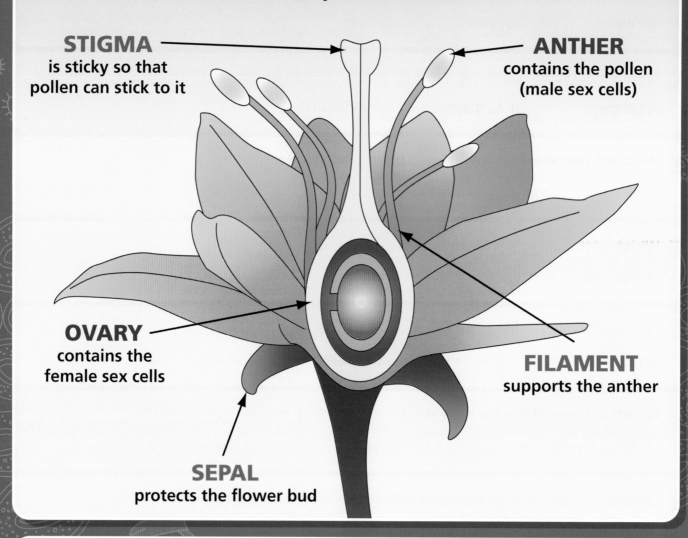

STIGMA
is sticky so that
pollen can stick to it

ANTHER
contains the pollen
(male sex cells)

OVARY
contains the
female sex cells

FILAMENT
supports the anther

SEPAL
protects the flower bud

The reproductive organs are inside the flower.

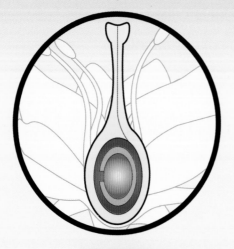

CARPEL
female reproductive organ

STAMEN
male reproductive organ

Quiz

Circle the correct answers.

1. **Is the stigma sticky?**

   a) Yes   b) No

2. **What sticks to the stigma?**

   a) Carpel   b) Anther   c) Pollen

3. **What are the two reproductive organs?**

   a) Ovary and Filament   b) Carpel and Stamen   c) Anther and Stigma

4. **Which of these is the male reproductive organ?**

   a) Stamen   b) Ovary   c) Filament

5. **What is inside an ovary?**

   a) Male sex cells   b) Female sex cells   c) Seeds

6. **Which of these is the female reproductive organ?**

   a) Sepal   b) Ovary   c) Carpel

7. **Why is the stigma sticky?**

   a) To Catch Pollen   b) To Attract Bees   c) For Protection

8. **What forms the base of a flower?**

   a) Receptacle   b) Sepal   c) Leaf

9. **What makes up a stamen?**

   a) Anther and Filament   b) Stigma and Style   c) Filament and Stigma

10. **What name is given to flowers with both male and female sex organs?**

    a) Hermaphrodite   b) Herbivorous   c) Homovorous

How many have you answered correctly?

/10

FOOD CHAINS

Living things depend on other living things for food.

THE FOOD CHAIN

Living things are split into two groups: **producers** and **consumers**.

PRODUCERS   ## CONSUMERS

Producers

Plants make their own food from the sun's energy.

Primary Consumers

Animals that only eat producers.

Secondary Consumers

Animals that eat primary consumers.

Tertiary Consumers

Animals that eat secondary consumers.

TYPES OF CONSUMER

Carnivores

Animals that eat other animals.

Top Carnivores

Animals that are not eaten by other living things.

Herbivores

Animals that eat only plants.

Omnivores

Animals that eat plants and other living things.

Quiz

Circle the correct answers.

1 There are two groups in a food chain, producers and . . . ?

a) customers   b) consumers   c) categories

2 With what do food chains begin?

a) Animals   b) Minerals   c) Plants

3 Green plants make their own food.

a) True   b) False

4 Which of these is a primary consumer?

a) Snail   b) Mouse   c) Cat

5 What sort of consumer is first in the food chain?

a) Primary   b) Secondary   c) Tertiary

6 What type of consumer is this animal?

a) Herbivore   b) Carnivore   c) Omnivore

7 From where do plants get energy?

a) Animals   b) Seeds   c) The Sun

8 What type of consumer is this animal?

a) Herbivore   b) Carnivore   c) Omnivore

9 What sort of consumer is second in the food chain?

a) Primary   b) Secondary   c) Tertiary

10 What type of consumer is this animal?

a) Herbivore   b) Carnivore   c) Omnivore

How many have you answered correctly?

/10

HABITATS

The place in which a plant or animal lives is called its habitat.
The habitat must have everything that a living thing needs to survive.

TYPES OF HABITAT

A DESERT

THE ARCTIC

A POND

THE SEASHORE

WOODLAND

A MEADOW

What animals need from their habitat:

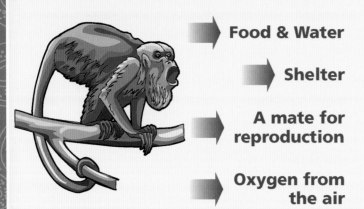

➡ Food & Water

➡ Shelter

➡ A mate for reproduction

➡ Oxygen from the air

What plants need from their habitat:

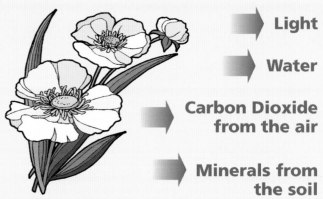

➡ Light

➡ Water

➡ Carbon Dioxide from the air

➡ Minerals from the soil

Animals and plants are adapted to survive in their habitat.

To survive in the arctic a polar bear:

- has a thick hairy coat and a layer of blubber to prevent heat escaping.
- has white fur for camouflage.
- is a strong swimmer and runner to catch food.
- has big feet to spread its weight on snow or ice.

To survive in the desert a cactus:

- has long roots to absorb water deep underground.
- has a thick fleshy stem to store water and a thick waxy coating to stop the water from evaporating.
- has sharp spines to stop herbivores eating it.

Quiz

Circle the correct answers.

1. The place where an organism (plant or animal) lives is called it's . . . . ?

   a) colony   b) habitat   c) population

2. When animals or plants are well suited to their habitat we say they are . . . . ?

   a) advantaged   b) adapted   c) connected

3. Which plant's habitat is the desert?

   a) Lilly   b) Tulip   c) Cactus

4. Which of the following do plants need from their habitat to survive?

   a) Oxygen   b) Shelter   c) Carbon Dioxide

5. Which of the following do animals need from their habitat to survive?

   a) Oxygen   b) Carbon Dioxide   c) Soil

6. Which animal has spots for camouflage to help it hunt?

   a) Lion   b) Tiger   c) Leopard

7. Polar bears have big feet to help them to . . . . ?

   a) keep body heat in   b) spread their weight   c) store food

8. Fish are adapted for swimming as they have a streamlined shape.

   a) True   b) False

9. Why does a cactus have spines?

   a) For Storage   b) For Camouflage   c) For Defence

10. How is a frog adapted for catching flies?

    a) It has webbed feet   b) It has slimy skin   c) It has a sticky tongue

How many have you answered correctly?

/10

SCIENTIFIC ENQUIRY

PLANNING

- Effective planning is essential.
- Outline a plan for your investigation.
- Decide what information you need to collect.
- Decide what you will observe and measure.
- Consider what apparatus and equipment you need.
- Describe and assess any hazards in your investigation.

INVESTIGATION

- Make sure your experiment is a fair test.
- Obtain your information carefully through accurate observation and measurement.
- Repeat your measurements and observations to ensure that the information is reliable.
- Record your results clearly.

ANALYSIS & EVALUATION

- Use the most effective way to present your results (table, graph, pie chart etc.).
- Analyse the information. Are there any trends or patterns?
- Draw conclusions from the results.
- Consider the strength of your evidence. Can you make any improvements to the process? What would you do differently?

Quiz

Circle the correct answers.

1. What is the first stage of scientific enquiry?

   a.) Evaluation   b.) Analysis   c.) Planning

2. Is effective planning essential?

   a.) Yes   b.) No

3. An investigation needs to be . . . ?

   a.) hard   b.) easy   c.) fair

4. What are hazards?

   a.) Warnings   b.) Concerns   c.) Risks

5. In which category would the sentence 'Record your results clearly' come?

   a.) Planning   b.) Investigation   c.) Analysis and Evaluation

6. How should you record your results?

   a.) Clearly   b.) Roughly   c.) Mentally

7. In which category would the sentence 'Draw conclusions from your results' come?

   a.) Planning   b.) Investigation   c.) Analysis and Evaluation

8. What can you draw from your results?

   a.) Summary   b.) Introduction   c.) Conclusions

9. In which category would the sentence 'Effective planning is essential' come?

   a.) Planning   b.) Investigation   c.) Analysis and Evaluation

10. What should you look for in your results?

    a.) Neatness   b.) Trends   c.) Outcomes

How many have you answered correctly?

/10

THE WATER CYCLE

Water is constantly moving between sea, air and land.

SUN SHINES

CONDENSATION

CONDENSATION

As air rises it cools and **condenses**. It reaches the ground as rain, snow, sleet or hail.

SNOW FORMS

SNOW MELTS AND FLOWS

EVAPORATION

EVAPORATION

LAKES FORM

EVAPORATION

EVAPORATION

Heat from the sun evaporates water.

EVAPORATION

EVAPORATION

WATER IS HEATED

RIVERS FLOW TO THE SEA

Evaporation - liquid changes to gas when warmed.
Condensation - gas changes to liquid when cooled.

Quiz

Circle the correct answers.

1 In the water cycle, what heats the water?

a) Sun   b) Fire   c) Snow

2 What is a natural water channel usually known as?

a) A Moat   b) A River   c) A Canal

3 To where do rivers flow?

a) Forests   b) The Sea   c) Mountains

4 Snow that has melted turns to . . . ?

a) ice   b) frost   c) water

5 By what process does a liquid change to a gas?

a) Condensation   b) Evaporation   c) Respiration

6 Where is snow most likely to fall?

a) High Ground   b) Low Ground   c) Cities

7 The starting point of a river is higher than its end point.

a) True   b) False

8 A water cycle is a sequence of processes that are . . . ?

a) reported   b) repeated   c) requested

9 Sea water is salty but river water is not.

a) True   b) False

10 Snow, sleet and hail are sometimes called . . . ?

a) presupposition   b) precipitation   c) perspiration

How many have you answered correctly?

/10

29

SOLIDS

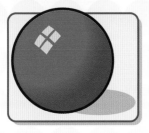

SNOOKER BALL

FORK

WOOD

PROPERTIES OF SOLIDS

Solids cannot easily be compressed.

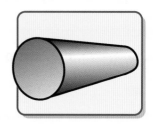

Solids can be cut.

Solids are easily controlled.

Solids cannot flow.

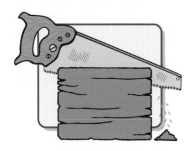

Solids have definite volumes and definite shapes.

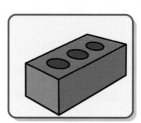

Look at the particles of a solid. It will help explain the above properties.

There are very strong forces of attraction between particles.

The particles are held tightly by strong forces and can hardly move.

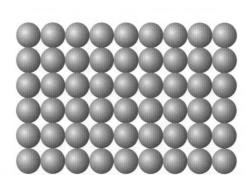

Solids cannot easily be compressed because the particles are very close together.

There are lots of particles in a given volume.

Quiz

Circle the correct answers.

1 Which of these is a solid?

a) Water   b) Helium   c) Fork

2 Can solids flow?

a) Yes   b) No

3 Which of these is a property of a solid?

a) Solids cannot be cut.   b) Solids can flow.   c) Solids are easily controlled.

4 Solids are easily compressed.

a) True   b) False

5 Which of these is a property of a solid?

a) Solids have definite volumes and definite shapes.   b) Solids can flow.   c) Solids are not easily controlled.

6 Particles of a solid are held tightly and . . . ?

a) can hardly move   b) can move about   c) are invisible

7 What sort of force acts between particles in a solid?

a) Protraction   b) Attraction   c) Distraction

8 Which of the pictures shows the particles of a solid?

a)   b)   c)

9 Particles in a solid are far apart.

a) True   b) False

10 Another word for 'compressed' is . . . ?

a) squeezed   b) pinched   c) stretched

How many have you answered correctly?

/10

LIQUIDS

WATER

VINEGAR

ORANGE JUICE

PROPERTIES OF LIQUIDS

Liquids cannot be cut.

Liquids take the shape of their containers.

Liquids are quite difficult to control.

Liquids flow.

Liquids have a definite volume.

Liquids cannot easily be compressed.

Look at the particles of a liquid. It will help explain the above properties.

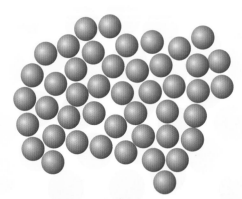

There are quite strong forces of attraction between particles.

The particles move constantly because they are not held as strongly as in solids.

Liquids which completely fill a container cannot easily be compressed because the particles are held close together.

There are lots of particles in a given volume.

Quiz

LIQUIDS

Circle the correct answers.

1 Which of these is a liquid?

   a) Oxygen   b) Vinegar   c) Wood

2 Which of these is a property of a liquid?

   a) Liquids can be cut.   b) Liquids don't flow.   c) Liquids have a definite volume.

3 Which of these is a property of a liquid?

   a) Liquids cannot be cut.   b) Liquids are easy to control.   c) Liquids don't have a definite volume.

4 Which of these liquids is used in cars?

   a) Vinager   b) Petrol   c) Cola

5 Particles of a liquid are very far apart.

   a) True   b) False

6 Which property is defined for a liquid?

   a) Volume   b) Shape   c) Area

7 Liquid particles are not held together tightly, so liquids . . . ?

   a) can't move   b) can move   c) are invisible

8 What sort of force acts between particles in a liquid?

   a) Protraction   b) Distraction   c) Attraction

9 Do liquids take up the shape of their containers?

   a) Yes   b) No

10 Which of the pictures shows the particles of a liquid?

   a)    b)   c)

How many have you answered correctly?  /10

33

GASES

HELIUM

OXYGEN

HYDROGEN

PROPERTIES OF GASES

Gases do not have a definite volume.

Gases cannot be cut.

Gases fill any available space.

Gases can easily be compressed.

Gases are hard to control.

Gases flow easily.

Most gases are invisible and spread into open spaces

Look at the particles of a gas. It will help explain the above properties.

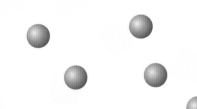

There are very weak forces of attraction between the particles.

The particles are far apart and move freely.

Gases can easily be compressed because there is plenty of space for the particles to move into.

There are few particles in a given volume.

Quiz

GASES

Circle the correct answers.

1 Which of these is a gas?

a) Carbon Dioxide　　　　b) Water　　　　c) Ice

2 When water is heated which gas is formed?

a) Helium　　　　b) Oxygen　　　　c) Steam

3 Can gases flow?

a) Yes　　　　b) No

4 Which of these is a property of gas?

a) Gases are easy to control.　　　　b) Gases do not have a definite volume.　　　　c) Gases can be cut

5 Particles of gas are . . . ?

a) close together　　　　b) far apart　　　　c) held tightly

6 Which of these is a property of gas?

a) Gases have a definite volume.　　　　b) Gases do not spread into open spaces.　　　　c) Gases fill any available space.

7 Gas particles are held together weakly so gases . . . ?

a) can't move　　　　b) can move freely　　　　c) are invisible

8 Do gases fill any available space?

a) Yes　　　　b) No

9 Which of the pictures shows the particles of a gas?

a)　　　　b)　　　　c)

10 Which of these gases do our lungs need to breathe?

a) Oxygen　　　　b) Hydrogen　　　　c) Helium

How many have you answered correctly?

/10

35

CHANGING MATERIALS

Some changes can be reversed and some cannot.

PHYSICAL CHANGES

Physical changes **can** be reversed.

FREEZING

This is when a liquid changes into a solid (by losing heat).

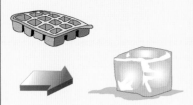

To reverse this change you heat.

MELTING

This is when a solid changes to a liquid (by gaining heat).

To reverse this change you cool.

DISSOLVING

This is when a solid dissolves if mixed with a solvent like water.

To reverse this change you heat.

EVAPORATING

This is when a liquid turns slowly into a gas (by gaining heat).

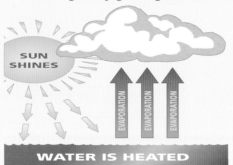

SUN SHINES

EVAPORATION EVAPORATION EVAPORATION

WATER IS HEATED

To reverse this change you cool.

CONDENSING

This is when a gas changes into a liquid (by losing heat).

To reverse this change you heat.

CHEMICAL CHANGES

Chemical changes **cannot** be reversed.

When **wood** burns it turns to **ash.**

Ingredients are baked to make a **cake.**

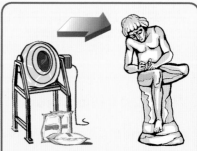

Sand, water and **cement** are mixed to form **concrete.**

Quiz

CHANGING MATERIALS

Circle the correct answers.

1 When steam cools on a plate, what is found on the plate?

a) Snow   b) Water   c) Ice

2 There are two types of change: one is physical, the other is . . . ?

a) chemical   b) electrical   c) structural

3 Which type of change can be reversed?

a) Biological   b) Chemical   c) Physical

4 Which of these processes changes water into ice?

a) Freezing   b) Melting   c) Dissolving

5 How many types of physical change are possible?

a) 3   b) 4   c) 5

6 Which of these processes changes water into water vapour?

a) Freezing   b) Evaporating   c) Condensing

7 When wood is burnt, what does it turn into?

a) Trees   b) Coal   c) Ash

8 Making concrete involves a . . . ?

a) chemical change   b) physical change   c) electrical change

9 What process happens when a solid changes to a liquid?

a) Condensing   b) Dissolving   c) Melting

10 When a solid breaks up in a liquid, what is it called?

a) Dissolving   b) Melting   c) Evaporating

How many have you answered correctly?

/10

SEPARATING MIXTURES

SIEVING

Can separate large particles from small particles.

SIEVE

- The sand and rock mixture is shaken through.

- The small holes in the sieve let the sand particles through and prevent the larger rocks from passing through.

FILTRATION

Can separate solids that are insoluble from a liquid.

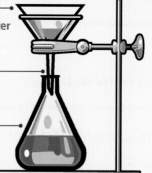

FILTER PAPER

Sand gathers in the filter paper. Water passes through.

FUNNEL

Channels the water into the flask.

FLASK

Gathers the water after filtration.

EVAPORATION

Can separate solids that are soluble from a liquid.

SALT WATER

EVAPORATING DISH

Water evaporates into the air, leaving only the salt.

BUNSEN BURNER

Heats the salt water so that it boils and turns to steam.

CONDENSATION

Condensing is when water vapour changes into liquid water.

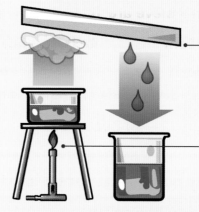

COLD SURFACE

The steam hits the surface and condenses into water droplets.

BUNSEN BURNER

Heats the water so that it boils and turns to steam.

CHROMATOGRAPHY

Can separate different colour dyes.

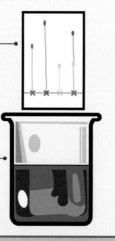

PAPER

- Spots of ink are placed on a pencil line.

- Solvent soaks up to the ink and each colour seeps upwards at a different rate.

SOLVENT

The paper is placed in the solvent which soaks up to the ink spots.

DISTILLATION

Can separate a solvent from a solution.

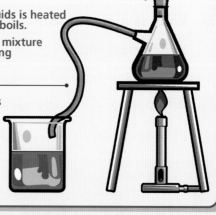

FLASK

- A mixture of liquids is heated from below and boils.

- The water in the mixture evaporates leaving the remainder.

CONDENSER

Steam condenses in the tube.

BEAKER

Pure, distilled water collects in the beaker.

Quiz

SEPARATING MIXTURES

1. How many ways are there of separating mixtures?

   a) 4   b) 5   c) 6

2. What is used to separate large particles from small particles?

   a) Bunsen Burner   b) Sieve   c) Flask

3. How many of the separating processes need heat?

   a) 2   b) 3   c) All

4. Which process is linked with colours?

   a) Sieving   b) Chromatography   c) Filtration

5. If the holes in a sieve are 1cm across, what size particles will pass through?

   a) More than 1cm   b) Less than 1cm   c) 2cm

6. To separate very small stones from water, which process is simplest?

   a) Sieving   b) Filtration   c) Evaporation

7. Condensing is when water vapour changes into . . . ?

   a) ice   b) liquid water   c) steam

8. Which process separates insoluble solids from a liquid?

   a) Evaporation   b) Distillation   c) Filtration

9. What is a liquid capable of dissolving other substances called?

   a) Solvent   b) Insolvent   c) Soluble

10. Which process separates a solvent from a solution?

    a) Evaporation   b) Distillation   c) Filtration

How many have you answered correctly?

/10

39

ELECTRICAL CIRCUITS

Electric current is the flow of charge around a circuit.

CIRCUIT

Electric current can only flow if there is a complete circuit:
any gaps will stop the current flowing.

SERIES CIRCUIT

The electrics in computers, stereos
and televisions contain series circuits.

CLOSED
CIRCUIT

OPEN
CIRCUIT

- The current takes only one path.
- The current is constant at all points
  in the circuit.

- The current can be turned on (switch
  closed) or off (switch open).

PARALLEL CIRCUIT

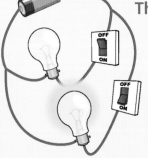

The mains electricity in a house is a parallel circuit,
allowing appliances to be used independently.

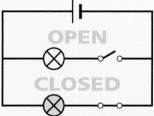

OPEN

CLOSED

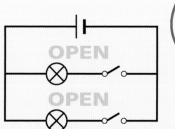

OPEN

OPEN

- The current takes more than one path.
- The current is constant from the beginning
  to the end of a path.

- Switches can be turned on or off to
  allow or restrict the flow to one or more
  parts of the circuit.

Quiz

Circle the correct answers.

1. Will electric current flow if there's gap in the circuit?

   a) Yes   b) No

2. Current will only flow if the circuit is . . . ?

   a) round   b) complete   c) serial

3. S is for series and P is for . . . ?

   a) periodic   b) plural   c) parallel

4. Circle the switch.

   a) 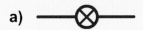   b) 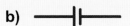   c)

5. In a series circuit, the current only takes one path.

   a) True   b) False

6. If all elements are working correctly, which circuit is correct?

   a) 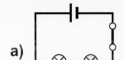   b) 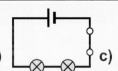   c)

7. What type of circuit is used in computers?

   a) Series   b) Parallel   c) Periodic

8. Circle the battery.

   a)    b)    c)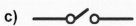

9. Circle the bulb.

   a) 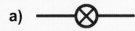   b)    c)

10. Is the current in a parallel circuit the same everywhere?

    a) Yes   b) No

How many have you answered correctly?

/10

CIRCUIT SYMBOLS

Electrical circuit diagrams can sometimes look confusing.
Here is an explanation of the most commonly used symbols.

 Cell | A cell is a source of electrical energy. |

 Battery | A battery contains numerous cells connected so that they produce more electrical energy. |

 Bulb | A bulb will light up only when it is in a circuit that is complete. |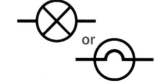

 Switch | A switch can be turned on (closed) to let current flow or turned off (open) to stop current flow. |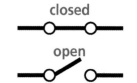

 **Motor** | A motor turns current into motion, for example, in a hair dryer. |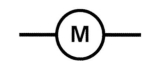

 **Buzzer** | A buzzer turns current into sound. |

 Ammeter | An ammeter is used to measure current. |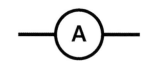

 Fixed Resistor | A fixed resistor controls the amount of current in a circuit. |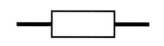

 Variable Resistor | A variable resistor can be adjusted to control the amount of current in a circuit. |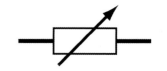

Quiz

Circle the correct answers.

1) To which of the pictures on the right does this symbol refer?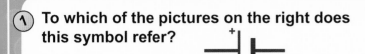
   a)   b)   c)

2) Which sign is on the battery symbol?
   a) x   b) +   c) £

3) Which letter is on the motor sign?
   a) N   b) C   c) M

4) To which of the symbols on the right does this picture refer?
   a) 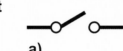   b) 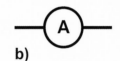   c)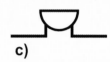

5) If a bulb lights up, in what sort of circuit is it?
   a) Complete   b) Incomplete   c) Open

6) To which of the symbols on the right does this picture refer?
   a) 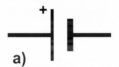   b) 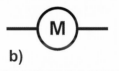   c)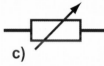

7) Which of these images shows a battery with two cells?
   a)   b)   c)

8) To which of the pictures on the right does this symbol refer?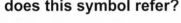
   a)   b)   c)

9) A buzzer turns current into sound.
   a) True   b) False

10) To which of the pictures on the right does this symbol refer?
   a)   b)   c)

How many have you answered correctly?

ELECTRICITY & MATERIALS

ELECTRICAL CONDUCTORS

Electricity can pass through some materials. We call these electrical conductors. Most good conductors are metals.

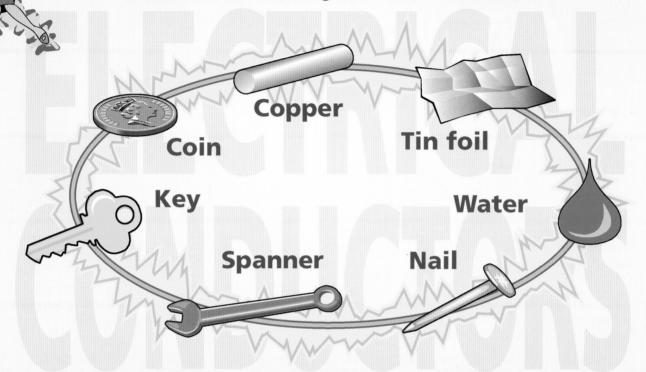

Copper

Coin

Tin foil

Key

Water

Spanner

Nail

ELECTRICAL INSULATORS

Electricity cannot pass easily through some materials. We call these electrical insulators. Electrical insulators are non-metals.

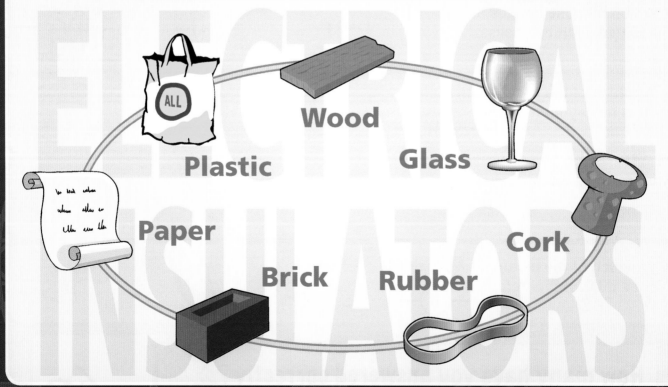

Wood

Plastic

Glass

Paper

Cork

Brick

Rubber

Quiz
ELECTRICITY & MATERIALS

Circle the correct answers.

1 Which of these is an electrical conductor?

a) Brick b) Wood c) Copper

2 Most electrical conductors are . . . ?

a) glass b) plastics c) metals

3 Which of these is an electrical insulator?

a) Spanner b) Key c) Glass

4 The opposite of 'conductor' is . . . ?

a) insulator b) predictor c) inductor

5 Which of these is an electrical conductor?

a) Paper b) Spanner c) Wood

6 Which of these conductors is not a solid?

a) Foil b) Water c) Coin

7 Which of these is an electrical insulator?

a) Wood b) Key c) Tin Foil

8 Electricity passes easily through an insulator.

a) True b) False

9 Which of these is the odd one out?

a) Glass b) Key c) Water

10 Why is water dangerous near electrical equipment?

a) It Conducts b) It Insulates c) It Flows

How many have you answered correctly?

/10

45

MAGNETS

A magnet is an object that has a magnetic field. Permanent magnets do not rely upon outside influences to generate their field. They occur naturally in some rocks. Electromagnets rely upon electric current to generate a magnetic field.

MAGNETS AND MAGNETIC MATERIALS

- A magnet is a piece of magnetic material with a **North** and a **South** pole.

- Metals such as iron, steel, nickel and cobalt are attracted by magnets. These are called magnetic materials. Not all magnetic materials are magnets.

MAGNETIC FIELDS

There is a magnetic field around every magnet.

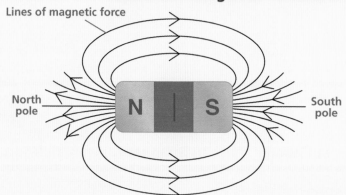

Lines of magnetic force

North pole

South pole

- Magnetic field lines always point from North to South.

- The magnetic field is always strongest near the poles of the magnet.

We can see these lines of force by using iron filings or a plotting compass. Iron filings will follow the magnetic field lines. The compass will always point from North to South along the magnetic field lines.

ATTRACTION AND REPULSION

When two magnets are placed next to each other they either **attract** each other or repel each other.

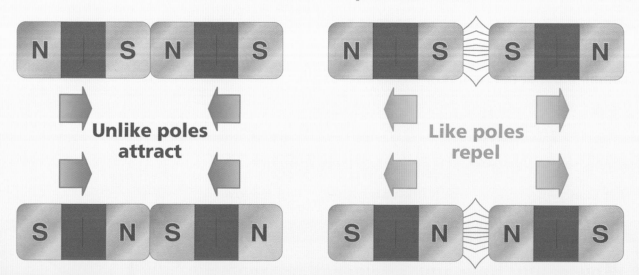

Unlike poles attract

Like poles repel

Quiz

Circle the correct answers.

1 What do we call the ends of a magnet?

a) Bars   b) Fields   c) Poles

2 What word is used to describe magnets moving closer together due to a magnetic force?

a) Attraction   b) Attrition   c) Friction

3 Will these 2 magnets attract or repel each other?

a) Attract   b) Repel

4 What word is used to describe magnets moving away from each other due to a magnetic force?

a) Revulsion   b) Repulsion   c) Friction

5 Will these 2 magnets attract or repel each other?

a) Attract   b) Repel

6 What do we call the lines of force surrounding a magnet?

a) Magnetic Meadow   b) Magnetic Field   c) Magnetic Valley

7 The magnetic field is strongest near the poles of a magnet.

a) True   b) False

8 In which direction do magnetic field lines point?

a) North to South   b) South to North   c) East to West

9 A small magnet that will point to the North pole of the Earth is called a . . . . ?

a) clock   b) compass   c) computer

10 Iron filings can be used to help you see the field lines around a magnet.

a) True   b) False

How many have you answered correctly? /10

FORCES

Forces are pushes or pulls.
Forces always have a direction in which they act.
We measure force in newtons - N.

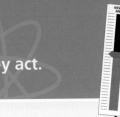

The man pushes the trolley away from him.

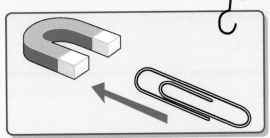

The force on the paper clip is towards the magnet.

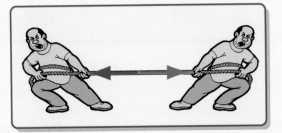

balanced force = no acceleration

unbalanced force = acceleration

What other forces are in these diagrams?

REMEMBER FORCES MAKE THINGS...

move

turn

go faster

slow down

change direction

change shape

GRAVITY is a force. It keeps us on the ground but also determines the movement of the stars and planets. The gravitational pull of the Earth attracts things to the centre of the Earth.

Quiz

Circle the correct answers.

1 Forces are pushes and . . . ?

a) pulls   b) drops   c) rushes

2 What units do we measure forces in?

a) Metres   b) Newtons   c) Kilograms

3 The pull of the Earth is called . . . ?

a) newtons   b) mass   c) gravity

4 Which arrow represents the force of the man pushing?

a)   b)

5 The scientific word for 'go faster' is . . . ?

a) accelerate   b) decelerate   c) increase

6 Which arrow represents the force of the magnet?

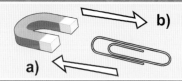

b)

a)

7 An instrument for measuring the size of a force is a . . . ?

a) weight balance   b) spring balance   c) force balance

8 Which set of arrows represents the correct forces?

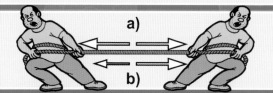

a)

b)

9 The opposite of 'accelerate' is . . . ?

a) sustain   b) increase   c) decelerate

10 Which set of arrows represents the correct forces?

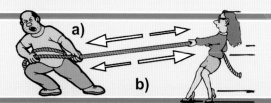

a)

b)

How many have you answered correctly?

/10

FRICTION

Friction occurs when two surfaces meet and rub against each other.
Friction slows a moving object, but can help control the movement.

ROUGH SURFACES

Rough surfaces slow moving objects but can be helpful.

The friction between the rough gravel and the tyres slows the racing car down.

The friction between his boots and the rock surface helps the climber keep his grip.

HEAT

Friction produces heat.

Rubbing your hands together produces heat.

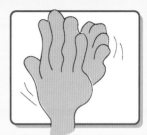

Rubbing two pieces of wood together can produce enough heat to create flames.

AIR RESISTANCE

Air resistance can affect motion: it can slow things down.

Gravity pulls this person down.

A small area means low air resistance and therefore a fast fall.

A large area means more air resistance and therefore a slower fall.

You can reduce air resistance by changing shape to become more streamlined.

The ski jumper tucks his arms in to reduce air resistance.

The cyclist tucks his head down to reduce air resistance.

This car is designed to be smooth and streamlined so that it goes fast.

Quiz

FRICTION

1 Friction occurs when two surfaces . . . ?

a) collide   b) rub   c) bounce

2 What is produced when friction occurs?

a) Sound   b) Light   c) Heat

3 What does friction do to a moving object?

a) Slows it down   b) Speeds it up   c) Nothing

4 Which of these is trying to increase air resistance?

a) Parachutist   b) Ski Jumper   c) Cyclist

5 Which of these is trying to reduce air resistance?

a) Parachutist   b) Cyclist   c) Plane Landing

6 What kind of friction does air produce?

a) Air Force   b) Air Rush   c) Air Resistance

7 Which of these has the lower air resistance?

a)   b)

8 It is very difficult to ride a bike across an ice-rink. Why?

a) Heat Build Up   b) High Friction   c) Low Friction

9 Which of these has the more air resistance?

a)   b)

10 Without friction we could not walk?

a) True   b) False

How many have you answered correctly?

/10

51

LIGHT

SUNLIGHT

Sunlight helps us in many ways:

For energy

To help things grow

For warmth

To see things

LIGHT SOURCES

Things that give out light are light sources (luminous objects):

Our Sun and other stars

Candle flame

Electric light bulb

PROPERTIES OF LIGHT

We see most objects because they reflect light from light sources into our eyes.

The speed of light is

300,000,000 METRES PER SECOND

Nothing travels faster than light, not even sound.

Light travels in straight lines.

Quiz

LIGHT

Circle the correct answers.

1 Is sunlight necessary for living things?

a) Yes   b) No

2 What do luminous objects do?

a) Give out Light   b) Absorb Light   c) Reflect Light

3 Light from the Sun provides us with warmth.

a) True   b) False

4 Sunlight helps plants to . . . ?

a) grow   b) fertilise   c) pollinate

5 We see most objects because they . . . ?

a) diffract light   b) deflect light   c) reflect light

6 Be careful! Light sources can be dangerous.

a) True   b) False

7 What luminous object gets smaller as you use it?

a) Candle   b) Bulb   c) Battery

8 Which of these is the brightest (most luminous) object?

a) Bulb   b) Flame   c) Sun

9 Into what can sunlight be turned?

a) Energy   b) Water   c) Candle

10 Does sound travel faster than light?

a) Yes   b) No

How many have you answered correctly?

/10

53

SHADOWS

When light hits an object, the light will either pass through it,
be absorbed by it, or bounce off it.

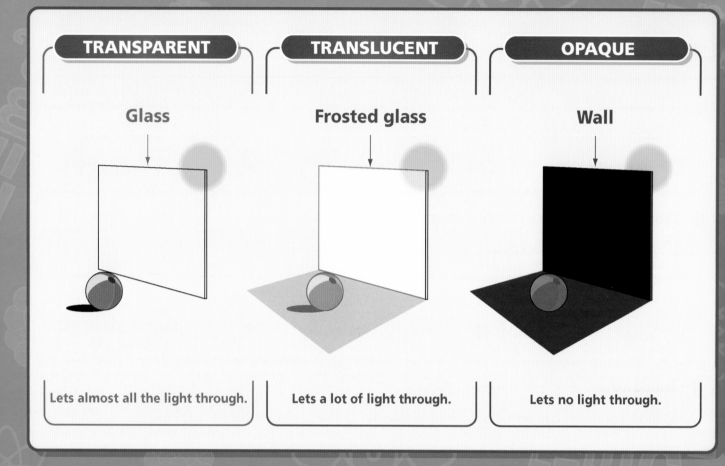

TRANSPARENT	TRANSLUCENT	OPAQUE
Glass	Frosted glass	Wall
Lets almost all the light through.	Lets a lot of light through.	Lets no light through.

**When light hits an opaque object it
cannot reach the other side. This causes a shadow.**

**If the light source is high
the shadows are short.**

**If the light source is low
the shadows are long.**

REMEMBER
Light travels in straight lines.

Quiz

SHADOWS

1. When light hits a transparent object, what happens?

   a) Passes Through   b) Gets Absorbed   c) Bounces Off

2. Which of these is transparent?

   a)    b)   c)

3. What is an everyday transparent material?

   a) Brick   b) Wood   c) Glass

4. Which of these is opaque?

   a)   b)   c)

5. Shadows are short when the light is . . . ?

   a) high   b) low   c) medium

6. Which of these is translucent?

   a)   b)   c)

7. In what sort of lines does light travel?

   a) Wavy   b) Straight   c) Curved

8. In the image, which is the correct light source?

   a)   b)   c)

9. What is caused in places where light can't reach the other side?

   a) Refractions   b) Shadows   c) Reflections

10. In the image, which is the correct light source?

    a)   b)   c)

How many have you answered correctly?

 /10

SOUND

If an object **vibrates** it may make a sound.

VIBRATION

Sound, unlike light, has to have a medium to carry the vibrations from the source to the ear.

Air vibrating

Air vibrating

Remember: you cannot always see what is vibrating.

SOUND THROUGH DIFFERENT MEDIUMS

Sound can travel through a variety of mediums and at different speeds.

Solid steel
6000m per second

Water
1500m per second

Air 20°C
340m per second
(Faster in warmer air)

VACUUM

Sound cannot travel through a vacuum.
There are no molecules to carry the vibrations.

ECHO

Like light, sound can be reflected from an object.
We call this an echo.

Quiz

Circle the correct answers.

1) Which part of a drum vibrates more?

a) The Skin   b) The Edge   c) Drumstick

2) Can you always see what is vibrating?

a) Yes   b) No

3) What picks up the sound of a singer?

a) Microscope   b) Microphone   c) Micrometer

4) Does sound travel through different substances?

a) Yes   b) No

5) What is an echo?

a) A Refracted Sound   b) A Reflected Sound   c) A Quiet Sound

6) Which of these is a vacuum?

a) Water   b) Air   c) Space

7) Does sound travel at the same speed through different sound mediums?

a) Yes   b) No

8) Through which of these does sound travel the quickest?

a) Steel   b) Air   c) Water

9) Through which of these can sound not travel?

a) Steel   b) Air   c) Space

10) Through which of these does sound travel the slowest?

a) Air   b) Steel   c) Water

How many have you answered correctly?

/10

AMPLITUDE AND PITCH

AMPLITUDE

Sound is a form of energy.

Low energy = quiet sound   **High energy = loud sound**

Intensity of sound is indicated by the height (amplitude) of the wave on an oscilloscope.

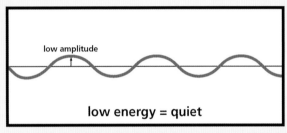 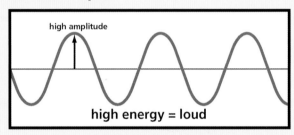

The further away you are from the source of the sound, the quieter the sound gets. This is because it spreads out and becomes dispersed.

PITCH

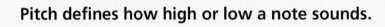

Pitch defines how high or low a note sounds.

For strings that are:

shorter
thinner   } = high pitch
tighter

For strings that are:

longer
thicker   } = low pitch
looser

Frequency, which measures the pitch of a note, is shown by the number of vibrations per second on an oscilloscope.

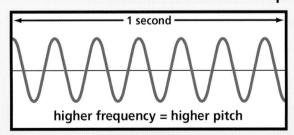 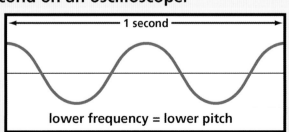

We measure sound frequency in hertz (Hz).

Quiz

Circle the correct answers.

1 Is sound quieter if you are far from the source?

a) Yes   b) No

2 When you shout, how much energy do you use?

a) A Lot   b) A Little   c) None

3 An oscilloscope is an instrument for showing the shape of sound waves.

a) True   b) False

4 Which of these oscilloscope shapes shows someone speaking the quietest?

 a)   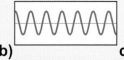 b)    c)

5 What does pitch mean when referring to sound?

a) A Field   b) Loudness   c) High or Low Notes

6 Amplitude is the height of a sound wave.

a) True   b) False

7 Which wave form shows a note of high energy?

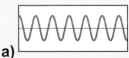 a)   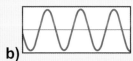 b)   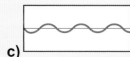 c)

8 Which wave form shows a note of high frequency?

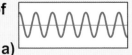 a)   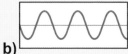 b)   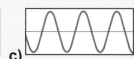 c)

9 A high-amplitude and high-frequency note is . . . ?

a) loud and low   b) loud and high   c) quiet and low

10 Which of these oscilloscope patterns shows the note of highest pitch?

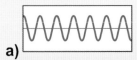 a)   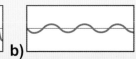 b)   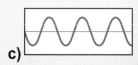 c)

How many have you answered correctly?   /10

59

EARTH'S SEASONS

As the Earth orbits the Sun, different parts tilt towards and away from the Sun.

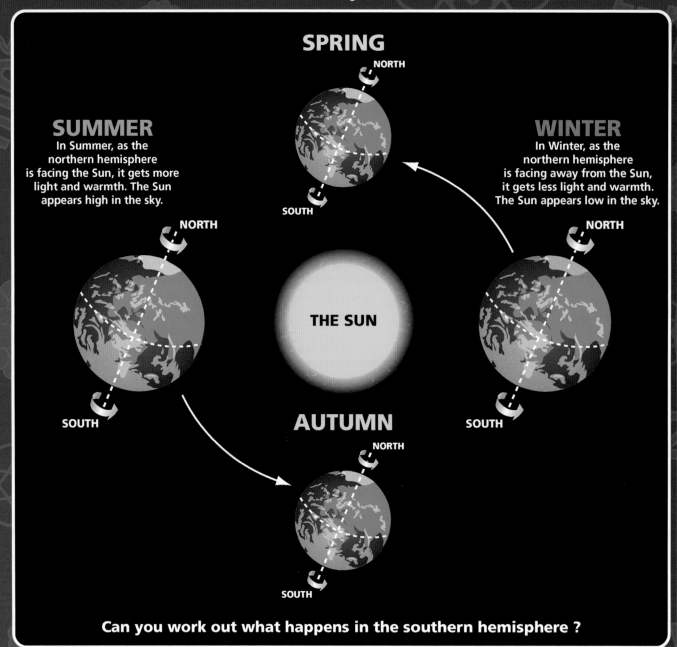

SPRING

NORTH

SOUTH

SUMMER
In Summer, as the northern hemisphere is facing the Sun, it gets more light and warmth. The Sun appears high in the sky.

NORTH

SOUTH

WINTER
In Winter, as the northern hemisphere is facing away from the Sun, it gets less light and warmth. The Sun appears low in the sky.

NORTH

SOUTH

THE SUN

AUTUMN

NORTH

SOUTH

Can you work out what happens in the southern hemisphere ?

The Sun's energy

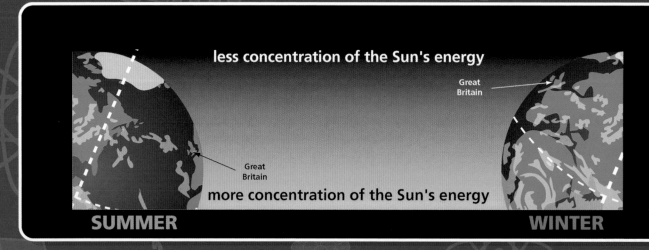

less concentration of the Sun's energy

Great Britain

Great Britain

more concentration of the Sun's energy

SUMMER

WINTER

Quiz

Circle the correct answers.

1. How many seasons are there in one year?

   a) 4   b) 12   c) 365

2. How many hemispheres does the Earth have?

   a) 1   b) 2   c) 4

3. Which season occurs after Winter?

   a) Summer   b) Spring   c) Autumn

4. The dotted line around the middle of the Earth is called the . . . ?

   a) tropics   b) equator   c) belt

5. What causes the Earth's seasons?

   a) Spin   b) Tilt   c) Wind

6. In which hemisphere is Great Britain?

   a) Northern   b) Southern   c) European

7. When does Britain receive the least concentration of the Sun's energy?

   a) Autumn   b) Winter   c) Spring

8. The dotted line from North to South of the Earth is called the . . . ?

   a) mountains   b) equator   c) axis

9. When it's Summer in Great Britain, what season is it in Australia?

   a) Summer   b) Autumn   c) Winter

10. Seasonal changes are the same all over the Earth.

    a) True   b) False

How many have you answered correctly?

/10

THE MOON

Our Moon is approximately spherical in shape. It orbits the Earth once every 27.3 days and its movement is determined by the gravitational pull of the Earth.

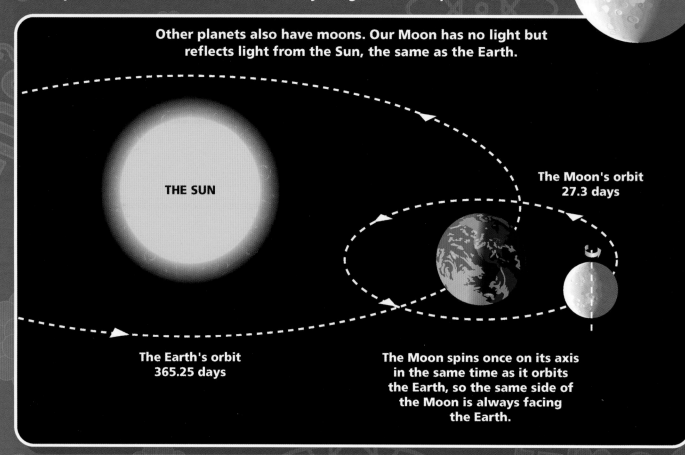

Other planets also have moons. Our Moon has no light but reflects light from the Sun, the same as the Earth.

THE SUN

The Moon's orbit
27.3 days

The Earth's orbit
365.25 days

The Moon spins once on its axis in the same time as it orbits the Earth, so the same side of the Moon is always facing the Earth.

Phases of the Moon

The Moon seems to us to change shape.
This depends on how much of the sunlit side we can see.

HALF MOON

THE SUN

NEW MOON

FULL MOON

HALF MOON

We call the time between full Moons a 'lunar month'.

FULL MOON   HALF MOON   NEW MOON   HALF MOON   FULL MOON

Quiz

Circle the correct answers.

1 What shape is the moon?

a) Spherical   b) Square   c) Triangular

2 How long does it take for the Moon to go around the Earth?

a) 30 days   b) 35 days   c) 27.3 days

3 From where does the Moon get its light?

a) Sun   b) Earth   c) Moon

4 Which of the diagrams shows a New Moon?

a)   b)   c)

5 The Earth travels around the . . . ?

a) Sun   b) Moon   c) Jupiter

6 Which of the diagrams shows a Full Moon?

a)   b)   c)

7 What is the path of the Moon around the Earth called?

a) Journey   b) Orbit   c) Track

8 Which of the diagrams shows a Half Moon?

a)   b)   c)

9 What is the time between two Full Moons called?

a) Lunar Month   b) Full Month   c) Calendar Month

10 What are the different shapes of the Moon called?

a) Angles   b) Shadows   c) Phases

How many have you answered correctly?

/10

Notes

Notes

Quiz Question Answers

The Human Skeleton   *Page 05*
1) b   2) a   3) c   4) a   5) c
6) c   7) a   8) b   9) c   10) a

The Heart and Circulation   *Page 07*
1) c   2) b   3) b   4) a   5) a
6) c   7) b   8) b   9) b   10) a

Teeth   *Page 09*
1) b   2) a   3) c   4) a   5) c
6) c   7) c   8) a   9) b   10) b

The Food Pyramid   *Page 11*
1) b   2) a   3) c   4) c   5) a
6) b   7) b   8) c   9) a   10) b

Health Risks   *Page 13*
1) c   2) b   3) b   4) b   5) a
6) b   7) a   8) a   9) c   10) b

Why Exercise?   *Page 15*
1) c   2) a   3) c   4) a   5) c
6) b   7) a   8) a   9) a   10) b

Parts of a Plant   *Page 17*
1) a   2) c   3) c   4) b   5) a
6) c   7) a   8) b   9) b   10) a

Life Cycle of a Plant   *Page 19*
1) b   2) b   3) b   4) a   5) c
6) c   7) a   8) b   9) c   10) b

Parts of a Flower   *Page 21*
1) a   2) c   3) b   4) a   5) b
6) c   7) a   8) b   9) a   10) a

Food Chains   *Page 23*
1) b   2) c   3) a   4) a   5) a
6) a   7) c   8) b   9) b   10) a

Habitats   *Page 25*
1) b   2) b   3) c   4) c   5) a
6) c   7) b   8) a   9) c   10) c

Scientific Enquiry   *Page 27*
1) c   2) a   3) c   4) c   5) b
6) a   7) c   8) c   9) a   10) b

The Water Cycle   *Page 29*
1) a   2) b   3) b   4) c   5) b
6) a   7) a   8) b   9) a   10) b

Solids   *Page 31*
1) c   2) b   3) c   4) b   5) a
6) a   7) b   8) b   9) b   10) a

Liquids   *Page 33*
1) b   2) c   3) a   4) b   5) b
6) a   7) b   8) c   9) a   10) c

Gases   *Page 35*
1) a   2) c   3) a   4) b   5) b
6) c   7) b   8) a   9) a   10) a

Changing Materials   *Page 37*
1) b   2) a   3) c   4) a   5) c
6) b   7) c   8) a   9) c   10) a

Separating Mixtures   *Page 39*
1) c   2) b   3) b   4) b   5) b
6) b   7) b   8) c   9) a   10) b

Electrical Circuits   *Page 41*
1) b   2) b   3) c   4) c   5) a
6) b   7) a   8) b   9) a   10) b

Circuit Symbols   *Page 43*
1) a   2) b   3) c   4) a   5) a
6) c   7) b   8) b   9) a   10) b

Electricity & Materials   *Page 45*
1) c   2) c   3) c   4) a   5) b
6) b   7) a   8) b   9) a   10) a

Magnets   *Page 47*
1) c   2) a   3) a   4) b   5) b
6) b   7) a   8) a   9) b   10) a

Forces   *Page 49*
1) a   2) b   3) c   4) b   5) a
6) a   7) b   8) a   9) c   10) a

Friction   *Page 51*
1) b   2) c   3) a   4) a   5) b
6) c   7) b   8) c   9) a   10) a

Light   *Page 53*
1) a   2) a   3) a   4) a   5) c
6) a   7) a   8) c   9) a   10) b

Shadows   *Page 55*
1) a   2) a   3) c   4) c   5) a
6) b   7) b   8) c   9) b   10) b

Sound   *Page 57*
1) a   2) b   3) b   4) a   5) b
6) c   7) b   8) a   9) c   10) a

Amplitude and Pitch   *Page 59*
1) a   2) a   3) a   4) a   5) c
6) a   7) b   8) a   9) b   10) a

Earth's Seasons   *Page 61*
1) a   2) b   3) b   4) b   5) b
6) a   7) b   8) c   9) c   10) b

The Moon   *Page 63*
1) a   2) c   3) a   4) b   5) a
6) c   7) b   8) a   9) a   10) c

Published by
Daydream Education
Unit 8, Denvale Trade Park, Ocean Way, Cardiff, CF24 5PF.
Tel: 0844 800 1660   Fax: 0844 800 1664

www.daydreameducation.co.uk

ISBN: 978-1-906248-50-5